For Susan, my practically perfect, Perry Aunt.

Penguin
sees a
Pear
in the
Park
from his
Paper Plane.

Penguin sees a Parrot playing the Piano from his Paper Plane.

Penguin
eats
Popcorn

at a puppet show in
his paper plane.

Penguin sees a Pig eating a

Pea from his Paper Plane.

Penguin sees people
doing a puzzle
from his paper plane.

Penguin
sees
a Peacock
with a
Purse
from his
Paper
Plane.

Penguin sees a Pirate with a

Pineapple from his Paper Plane

Penguin paints his
paper plane
pink and purple...

...to go to a party
at the South Pole!

words in
this book:

Penguin

PineaPPle

Pig

Pirate

PaPer Plane

Peacock

PuPPet

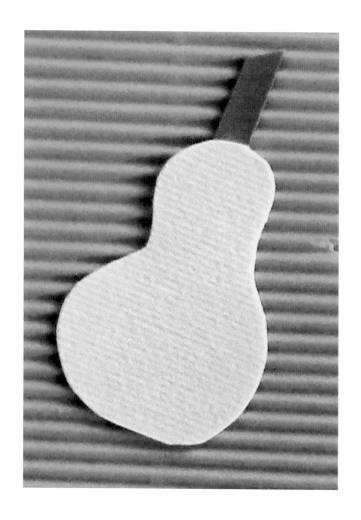

Pear

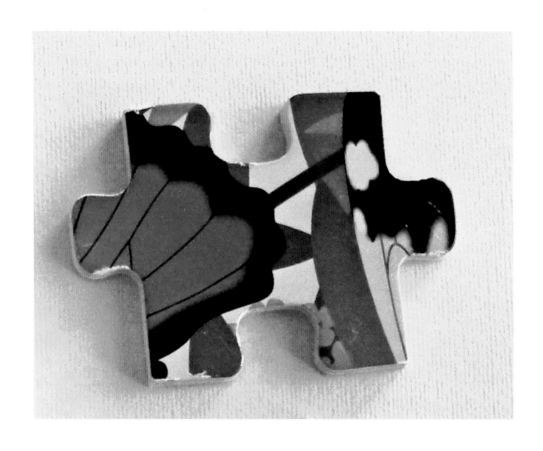

Puzzle

PoPcorn

Pink and PurPle Paint

Cutting **PAPER**
to make **PICTURES!**

P is for PAPER Art!

Penguin has a Pink and Purple, Paper Plane.

Make your own

PAPER

PICTURE

with colored paper, scissors, glue and your imagination!

AlphaBOX Book Series

APPLES AND APRICOTS
by H.P. Gentileschi
A

Boy on a Bus
by H.P. Gentileschi
B

Cat in a Cup
by H.P. Gentileschi
C

Duck's Days
by H.P. Gentileschi
D

Elephant's Easter Eggs
by H.P. Gentileschi
E

Is This a Fish?
by H.P. Gentileschi
F

Gorillas Like Gum
by H.P. Gentileschi
G

THIS HAND
by H.P. Gentileschi
H

INSECTS in my ICE-CREAM
by H.P. Gentileschi
I

When Do You Drink Juice?
by H.P. Gentileschi
J

WHERE IS KATE'S KEY?
by H.P. Gentileschi
K

I Like to Lick LOLLIPOPS
by H.P. Gentileschi
L

MILK in My Mailbox

by H.P. Gentileschi

M

DOES A NUT HAVE A NOSE?

by H.P. Gentileschi

N

ONE OCTOPUS in the Olive Tree

by H.P. Gentileschi

O

penguin's paper plane

by H.P. Gentileschi

P

The Queen's Question

by H.P. Gentileschi

Q

Rabbit's Rainbow in Rome

by H.P. Gentileschi

R

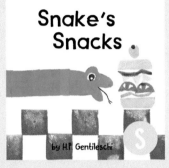

Snake's Snacks

by H.P. Gentileschi

S

Does a Tomato Have Teeth?

by H.P. Gentileschi

T

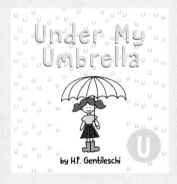

Under My Umbrella

by H.P. Gentileschi

U

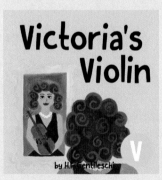

Victoria's Violin

by H.P. Gentileschi

V

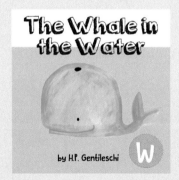

The Whale in the Water

by H.P. Gentileschi

W

Fox Has A Box

by H.P. Gentileschi

X

YOUR YELLOW YO-YO

by H.P. Gentileschi

Y

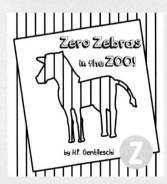

Zero Zebras in the ZOO!

by H.P. Gentileschi

Z

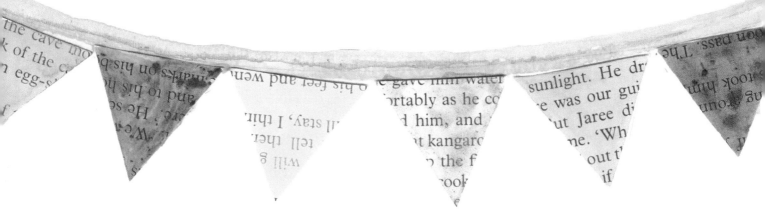

For more engaging activities, teaching resources and to learn more about AlphaBOX books, follow H.P. Gentileschi on:

H.P. Gentileschi

www.hpgentileschi.com

hpgentileschi@gmail.com

We'd love to see how you're using the AlphaBOX series!
Share and tag your photos using:
#alphaboxbooks

Made in the USA
Columbia, SC
01 February 2021

32139396R00018